Q&A

...*off the record*

Q&A

Picasso

...off the record

LIFE AND THEMES · 1881 · 1973

NEIL COX

Foreword by
SIMON SCHAMA

WATKINS PUBLISHING
LONDON

Picasso
Neil Cox

This edition first published in the United Kingdom and Ireland in 2010
by Watkins Publishing, an imprint of Duncan Baird Publishers Ltd
Sixth Floor, Castle House
75–76 Wells Street, London W1T 3QH

Conceived, created and designed by Duncan Baird Publishers

Managing Editors: Gill Paul and Peggy Vance
Co-ordinating Editor: James Hodgson
Editor: Jack Tresidder
Assistant Editor: Duncan Carson
Managing Designer: Clare Thorpe

British Library Cataloguing-in-Publication Data:
A CIP record for this book is available from the British Library
ISBN: 978-1-907486-63-0
10 9 8 7 6 5 4 3 2 1
Typeset in Dante MT and Baskerville BT
Printed in Shanghai by Imago

Publisher's note:
The interviews in this book are purely fictional, while having a solid
basis in biographical fact. They take place between a fictionalized
Pablo Picasso and an imaginary interviewer. This literary work has
not been approved or endorsed by the Picasso estate.

CONTENTS

FOREWORD by Simon Schama

Artists, Picasso said, "should invent, not just copy nature like an ape". If a two-dimensional duplicate of the world is wanted, the modernist argument ran, then photography is always going to supply that much more efficiently than painting. Since the 1860s, self-consciously modern art had defined itself as post-photographic, always seeking a different reason to be looked at, something other than a surface impression of the world. Before Cubism, modern painting had flirted with this break-up of coherence. Van Gogh, for instance, chose the colour of things and people according to emotive perception rather than optically observed hue. But around 1910 Picasso and his friend Georges Braque, stirred by Paul Cézanne's late destructions of solid form into crystallographically faceted structures that were somehow both broken and coherent at the same time, went for the kill. Bye-bye resemblance.

The departure from resemblance pointed in two directions: decoration or sculpture. The decorative way – chosen, for example, by Matisse – was the road to abstraction: shimmering arrangements of flat, brilliant colour designed to set our senses dancing and put a smile on our face. But Picasso, the least sentimental and the most sculptural of all modern artists, went the other way, wanting somehow to register the tactile in paint. Although he spoke of his cubist experiments as beginning in pure compositional painting, he also insisted that they were paintings of something other than themselves. Deep within the slinky-toy cubist unfurlings of form, seen as if juddering through time, was something substantial and concrete. The simultaneous multi-dimensional rendering of different aspects of a figure *was*, somehow, a representation of what that figure truly was. So no colours other than those of engineering and architecture – rusty browns, dusty ochres and steel greys – were to distract the viewer from the exposed scaffolding on which he hung that idea of fundamental form.

The provocation was entered into in the utmost good faith. By blowing up the apparent look of things – and people – the cubists were saying that they were offering an alternative reality, the reality of memory or shifting perception. "Any form that conveys to us the sense of reality," Picasso said many years later, "is the one *furthest* removed from the reality of the retina; the eyes of the artist are open to a superior reality; his works are evocations."

INTRODUCTION

The series of fictional dialogues in this book takes place during the last decade of Pablo Picasso's life in his last home, Notre-Dame-de-Vie, at Mougins in the south of France. As well as reported conversations, they are based on the artist's published statements, and the very few reliable interviews that were published during his lifetime. Picasso had a pathological objection to having his voice recorded – so virtually all the pronouncements attributed to him are the product of recollections jotted down by his friends after the fact. Some rushed home to log their observations; others only published them later and in some cases after their friendship with the artist had failed. Picasso managed a few words in the 1955 film *The Picasso Mystery* ("that's going badly!" he says of a painting in progress), but for all the reported speech there is little hard evidence for an accurate tone.

Most of those close to Picasso agree that he was not given to extended comments on art or on other serious topics, but preferred instead ironic *bons mots*, paradoxes and riddles. Some of his answers to my questions give a flavour of his mischievous love of irony. A real-life interviewer would have found it almost impossible to obtain such privileged access to the painter in his later years. I have presumed to engage Picasso in the kind of sincere intellectual discussion that was by all accounts only very rarely granted, and only to his most trusted friends.

The consequences of Picasso's complicated personal life added to this need for privacy. Married twice, but having also had many other relationships, Picasso left a trail of emotional destruction in his wake. Marie-Thérèse Walter, his lover of the 1920s and 1930s and the mother of his daughter Maya, committed suicide in 1977. His last wife, Jacqueline Roque, did the same in 1986. One of Picasso's three legitimate grandchildren, Pablito, died after drinking bleach in reaction to being excluded from the artist's home on his death. Pablito's sister Marina has written of the pain that the artist's selfish behaviour caused those around him, though her version of events is strongly contested by Maya's son, Olivier Widmaier-Picasso. These terrible stories hint at the same time at Picasso's enormous personal magnetism: although short in stature he was a commanding presence and charismatic in company. When Picasso wanted to turn on the charm, he trapped his victim in an intense black-eyed gaze. Lovers, friends, family and even museum curators all hankered after that feeling of intimacy, and would tolerate endless abuse in order to retain it.

Whatever we may think of Picasso as a person, he was the most renowned artist of the 20th century and one of the most prolific and important innovators in the history of modern art. There are four major museums that honour his genius: the Musée Picasso, Paris; the Musée Picasso, Antibes; the Museu Picasso, Barcelona; and the Museo Picasso, Málaga. Picasso's posthumous reputation is reflected in the fact that his *Boy with a Pipe* (1905), an oil of a Montmartre lad crowned with roses and loosely holding a pipe, sold for $104m in 2004 – a record at that time for a painting sold at auction. His work continues to be controversial, with some critics regarding large swathes of his output as whimsical daubs, others seeing him as the most important visual artist of our epoch. The aim of this book is not only to bring to life a man of unusual intelligence but also to encourage the reader to look afresh at Picasso's art.

PABLO PICASSO (1881–1973)

His Life in Short

Pablo Picasso was born on October 25, 1881, in Málaga, Andalusia. He failed to draw breath until a resourceful uncle blew cigar smoke into his nostrils. Pablo was the first-born child of relatively middle-class parents, Maria Picasso López and José Ruiz Blasco, a painter and aficionado of the bullfight. Both sides of the family traced aristocratic lineage, but by the time Pablo came along any grandeur had faded, and his father earned a modest living teaching drawing at Málaga's art school. Lola, the elder of Pablo's two sisters, was born in 1884, and Conchita in 1887. Pablo was devoted to his younger sister, whose death at the age of seven apparently traumatized him and made him sharply aware of his own mortality.

Pablo was by then already a budding artist, unwilling to study anything else at school. The earliest of his surviving drawings and paintings are those of a very able child, and represent bullfight scenes and pigeons – subjects inspired by the work of his father. The family had moved to La Coruña in northern Spain in 1891, where Pablo had been enrolled in his father's art school class. By 1895 or so, just after the death of Conchita, his charcoal studies of plaster casts from classical sculptures are impressive academic exercises, while painted portraits or animal subjects show a sudden leap in skill. But at the same time Pablo did schoolboy cartoons, and even invented his own magazine. At around this time he began to sign his drawings "P. Ruiz"; it was not until a few years later that he settled on "Pablo Picasso", using his mother's surname, as his preferred artistic identity. In 1895 the family moved once again. Picasso's father had a new job in the La Llotja art school in Barcelona. Picasso passed the entrance exam and joined an advanced class at the age of fourteen, delighted to be given the chance to draw from live models. It was around this time that Picasso first visited prostitutes, acquired his first girlfriend, and enjoyed the nightlife of a large city priding itself on northern European ties. All this new experience coincided with Picasso's first ambitious oil paintings, *First Communion* (1896) and *Science and Charity* (1897), a scene showing a sick or dying woman. These works were strongly influenced by his father's conservative notions of artistic achievement, and it was perhaps through his good offices that *Science and Charity* was given a medal in the fine arts exhibition in Málaga.

Picasso escaped his father's influence in his next move: to the Royal Academy art school in Madrid. Here, he skipped the school's still very formal training in favour of sketching city life and studying works by artists such as El Greco, Velázquez and Goya in the Prado museum. His laziness in formal studies alarmed his family elders, however, and subvention from his wealthy uncle was withdrawn, forcing his hard-up father to find the money. Picasso fell seriously ill on his poor diet in 1898 and decided to return to his beloved Barcelona. But first he convalesced in the mountain village of Horta de Ebro, staying with his friend Manuel Pallarés and adopting an outdoor, gypsy lifestyle. He returned to Barcelona in 1899 a confident and much more ambitious artist, and it was here that he became self-consciously a "modern", moving in literary-artistic circles influenced by art nouveau and symbolist ideas from Munich, Oslo, Paris and Vienna.

Picasso forged important new friendships with the painter Carles Casagemas and the poet Jaime Sabartés. The latter would remain a lifetime loyal friend to Picasso. He inducted Picasso into the work of Parisian illustrators Steinlen and Caran d'Ache, and introduced him to symbolist writings by Maeterlinck and Verlaine. Under these influences Picasso's art became sombre, and he painted *Last Moments*, a large work depicting a dying girl. The centre of action for avant-garde artists was a café known as Els Quatre Gats ("The Four Cats"), modelled on the "Bohemian" cafés of Montmartre so important to the work of the much-admired Toulouse-Lautrec whose friend Miquel Utrillo frequented the new Barcelona hang-out. Like Parisian cafés, Els Quatre Gats published its own magazine and staged various lively performances. Picasso's notoriety grew, especially after he exhibited 150 drawings of friends and notable figures at the café in a deliberate attempt to outdo a recent show by a more established artist. Undaunted by the poor critical response, Picasso was by now determined to put himself at the centre of modern art: so with Casagemas he travelled to Paris for the World Exhibition in October 1900.

Picasso was to visit Paris every year until 1904, when he settled there for good. His first visit was promising: he sold three pastels of bullfight scenes to the dealer Berthe Weill, and the Catalan dealer Pedro Mañach offered him a contract providing income of 150 francs a year. Picasso's art responded immediately to the context and the market: he made paintings that were conspicuously experimental, obviously Parisian, and often erotic in their subject matter. He moved in Bohemian and anarchist circles, without ever being drawn deeply into either. Picasso went back to Málaga with Casagemas, but abandoned him to return to Madrid in 1901. There, he learned that Casagemas had gone to Paris and, depressed by unrequited love for a woman, had shot himself in front of her and other friends in a restaurant.

By May 1901 Picasso was back in Paris, and Mañach managed to persuade the important dealer Ambroise Vollard to mount an exhibition of the young Spaniard's work. This caught the attention of some important critics, and was also the occasion of Picasso's first meeting with the poet Max Jacob, a great friend in coming years. Money problems meant a return to Spain. During his sojourn in Barcelona from January to October 1902, Picasso worked in a new predominantly blue palette on a monumental painting called *Two Sisters*, based on women seen at the prison of St Lazare in Paris, as well as some depictions inspired by Casagemas. Picasso's third visit to Paris in October

1902 was a disaster. He ended up sharing a room with Max Jacob, and managed to secure a place in a group show at Weill's in November, where he unveiled his blue paintings as well as pictures from 1901 in a lighter Parisian vein. But nothing sold, and Picasso despaired. The only consolation was a positive review from poet Charles Morice, who gave Picasso a precious printed copy of Paul Gauguin's Tahitian journal, *Noa-Noa*.

Penniless once again, Picasso returned to Barcelona in January 1903 until April 1904. During this time he produced the most important of his so-called "blue period" paintings, including *Life*, a title that – unusually – Picasso may have chosen himself. Once completed, the picture sold quickly, if not for a huge sum. Return to Paris was made possible by a vacancy in a studio building in Montmartre, nicknamed the Bateau-Lavoir (floating laundry), which was to be the scene of Picasso's rise to pre-eminence as one of the most radical artists of his day. It was here that Picasso gradually exchanged morose blue for delicate pink, and achieved a lyrical ambience close to that found in the early poetry of Guillaume Apollinaire. The new style was most prominently displayed in a huge painting of a group of circus acrobats, *Family of Saltimbanques* (1905). But his "rose period" was only the start of enormous changes in Picasso's art and life. He formed his first long-term relationship, with a woman called Fernande Olivier, made his first serious etchings, and was stimulated by retrospectives of the work of Ingres, Cézanne and Gauguin, and the revelations of current exhibitions. The group of artists labelled Fauves ("Wild Beasts") for their vividly coloured paintings at the Salon d'Automne of 1905 drew Picasso's attention to Henri Matisse, whose innovative work he soon challenged with *Les Demoiselles d'Avignon*, a hugely ambitious painting of five women in a brothel. The heads of the women closely resembled primitive Iberian sculptures in the Louvre, some of which he bought, perhaps not realizing they were stolen, perhaps knowingly. The painting was only completed during the summer of 1907 with the aid of a visit to the Trocadéro Museum, Paris, where he saw many African and Oceanic objects that prompted a re-working of heads in the painting.

So it was that, following the first aesthetically motivated purchases of tribal objects by the Fauves Vlaminck and Derain, Picasso appropriated the languages of non-Western art. Through this painting, he won the enthusiasm of a new and important dealer, Daniel-Henry Kahnweiler, and began to compete for the favours of new collectors. Although the violently dislocated forms of *Demoiselles* were not widely appreciated in Picasso's circles and the painting remained in his studio until the 1920s, it prompted a young painter named Georges Braque to work closely with him over the next seven years. These two artists, who met properly in 1908, invented an entirely new pictorial language: Cubism. Apart from the early cubist work *Composition with Death's Head*, which apparently commemorated the suicide of the drug-using German painter Wiegels, most of Picasso's figure and still-life paintings of the next years are devoid of obvious personal reference. Cubist paintings, if they have any such meaning, are coded by means of minimal identifying signs. Colour was initially reduced to a sombre palette of greys, browns and greens, while drawing served to produce strange shifts of perspective and spatial distortions. Braque's first show at Kahnweiler's in November 1908 led one critic to coin the "cube" epithet. And as Braque and Picasso became close and worked together to dismantle the traditions of representation in Western art, they also gradually withdrew from public exhibitions and relied on dealers like Vollard and Kahnweiler to sell their work. For Picasso the crucial early painting trips were to La Rue-des-Bois north of Paris in August 1908, and then Horta (once again) in summer 1909.

Picasso was a prolific artist (much more prolific than Braque), and his new relationship with Kahnweiler was profitable. Sales to Russian collectors were particularly good. Picasso and Fernande moved to a new and much more fashionable apartment on Boulevard de Clichy in autumn 1909, and held open house on Sundays. That autumn Picasso also began to create cubist sculptures, including a remarkable *Head of a Woman*, based on Fernande. By this time he was frequently taking photographs, used sculpture as an increasing part of his repertoire, and made extraordinary cubist etchings in 1910 to illustrate poems by Max Jacob. As Cubism developed, important trips were made out of Paris each summer: to Cadaqués (1910), Céret (1911, 1912, 1913), Sorgues (1912), and Avignon (1912, 1914). Cubist paintings of 1910 reached an extraordinary degree of sparseness verging on abstraction. By 1911–12 Braque and Picasso made further radical moves: typography was incorporated into paintings such as Picasso's *Ma Jolie*; Picasso used printed oil-cloth in a still-life oil painting; Braque introduced cut-out pieces of fake wood grain and newspaper into drawings; and finally Braque and Picasso began to make an entirely new kind of sculpture from cheap materials such as cardboard, sheet metal, wire and painted wood. Cubism appeared to celebrate the everyday, the beauty of found materials, and a new kind of visual language. At the same time Picasso's wealth continued to grow:

he took a new studio – replacing the Bateau-Lavoir – on Boulevard Raspail in 1912, and moved to a new flat on Rue Schoelcher in 1913.

Picasso's private life had become increasingly complicated. Prior to his involvement with Fernande, he had a succession of liaisons with various women, often showing little sensitivity as he moved abruptly from one to another. *Ma Jolie* appears to refer to Eva Gouel, a woman with whom Picasso got involved when his relationship with Fernande collapsed in 1911. Eva herself fell seriously ill in summer 1915, dying of cancer that December, and while she was in hospital Picasso began a liaison with Gaby Depeyre, whom he tried to marry. Her refusal prompted Picasso to court Irène Lagut, a would-be artist who was eventually replaced by his marriage to Russian dancer Olga Khokhlova in 1918. This turbulent love-life coincided with the most startling and humorous hybrid cubist constructions and paintings, and also with the advent of World War I, severing the ties between Frenchman Braque and (neutral) Spaniard Picasso, and bringing a bitter end to the enthusiasm and idealism of Picasso's early career. These changes coincided with Picasso's return to the classical idiom of Ingres to depict an artist and model in 1914. He followed this with Ingresque drawings of Jacob and Apollinaire, and some former admirers found the use of two contradictory styles – cubist and classical – difficult to accept. Apollinaire was wounded at the front in 1916, and died in 1918. Braque was also wounded, and took years to recover his confidence as an artist. Apollinaire's role as principal poet in Picasso's life was supplanted during the war by Jean Cocteau, an opportunistic cultural commentator (and later great film director) who engineered Picasso's involvement with the Ballet Russes. Picasso designed the set and costumes for a ballet called *Parade* in 1917, choreographed by Leonid Massine and with music by Erik Satie.

Picasso's post-war art was schizophrenic, oscillating between cubist and neo-classical idioms. His marriage to Olga announced his arrival as a bourgeois gentleman: they took rooms in the Hôtel Lutetia, and then bought a two-floor apartment on the desirable rue La Boétie. Picasso continued to work with the Ballet Russes in London in 1919 and Paris in 1920, 1922 and 1924. The couple spent each summer on the French Riviera, Picasso's art often seeming to reflect the notional idyll of a classical Mediterranean culture. Picasso's first son, Paulo, was born in 1921, a boy destined to suffer in the shadow of his father. He later became Picasso's chauffeur, succumbed to alcoholism and died of liver cancer in 1975. This would not be the last personal tragedy to follow in the artist's wake.

Cubism became a part of Picasso's identity as an artist, an idiom to which he constantly returned and that he often reinvented. A second great force came into Picasso's creative vocabulary in the mid-1920s: Surrealism. The leader of the surrealist movement, the poet André Breton, persuaded the fashion designer Jacques Doucet to buy Picasso's *Demoiselles* in 1922. Three years later, Breton included Picasso in the surrealist pantheon, and published abstract drawings by the artist in the second issue of the magazine *La Révolution Surréaliste*. Surrealism was in a sense a development of the idea of an art of dream and fantasy found in the Symbolism Picasso had come across in Barcelona circles before the turn of the century. But Surrealism was inflected with Freudian psychoanalysis, revolutionary Marxism, and a virulent avant-garde polemicism. For Picasso, who always remained slightly outside the politics of the movement, Surrealism represented a revitalization of his own avant-garde credentials, particularly via a revival of contact with radical poets and intellectuals dedicated to challenging bourgeois values through confrontations with non-Western art and popular culture. Picasso participated in the first exhibition of surrealist painting in November 1925, and Breton reinterpreted Picasso's cubist paintings and constructions as "surrealist" before the word existed. Apollinaire had invented it in his programme notes for *Parade* in 1917, and so Picasso's name was auspiciously associated with it.

Picasso's involvement with Surrealism brought him into contact with younger artists including the Catalans Dalí and Miró, and the Frenchman André Masson. He also formed a lifelong friendship with the writer and later ethnographer Michel Leiris. Most importantly, the ambit of Surrealism transformed Picasso's art. A sinister expressive deformation of the body combined with shrill decorative patterning that was almost a parody of cubist colour schemes to produce hysterical or erotic images of women in interiors. Bone-like creatures disported on beaches; virile bulls impaled horses and female matadors; blind or evicted Minotaurs representing man subject to his bestial instincts wandered desolate shores. Picasso's work of this period in paintings, sculpture, drawings, prints and book illustration is arguably his finest.

In January 1927, Picasso met the seventeen-year-old Marie-Thérèse Walter. He began an affair with her conducted in secret but commemorated in many remarkable works, most of which he made at the Château de Boisgeloup, bought in 1930. The tension between Picasso's married life and his clandestine affair was unsustainable, and by the time Marie-Thérèse was expecting a child in 1935 (christened Maya) Picasso separated from Olga, initiating an acrimonious legal wrangle over Olga's settlement that would force him to hand over Boisgeloup to her. During this turbulent period he made few works but wrote a large number of poetic texts. Picasso also became a major figure in the history of art: in 1932 a project was launched to document photographically his entire oeuvre (the first volume of a catalogue raisonné was published by Christian Zervos), and he was the subject of a retrospective exhibition in Paris.

The whole tenor of Picasso's surrealist vocabulary changed in 1936 with the outbreak of the Spanish Civil War. At the same moment, Picasso began a relationship with the talented photographer and painter Dora Maar. The civil war prompted a succession of now famous works: the satirical prints called *Dream and Lie of Franco*, the *Weeping Woman*, and, of course, *Guernica*. The last of these was Picasso's response to a commission in 1937 from the Republican Government to decorate their pavilion at the forthcoming world exhibition in Paris. The Basque town of Guernica was bombed by the Luftwaffe on 26 April that year, and Picasso, who had been floundering with the commission, suddenly found a focus for his surrealist bullfights and screaming women. *Guernica* was painted in a new studio on the rue des Grands Augustins. After being shown in the pavilion, it toured to England, and then ended up in New York for safekeeping. In accordance with Picasso's wishes, the painting was sent to its intended home in Spain only after the fall of Franco, and indeed therefore, after the artist's death.

Picasso's studio in rue des Grands Augustins was a gathering place for many during the Nazi occupation of Paris during World War II. Picasso appears to have been too well known for the Nazis to trouble him too much, and he was also careful not to overstep any lines of danger. He ate black market steaks in the restaurant opposite, but did not openly defy the regime. During the war Picasso made many austere and sometimes grotesque portraits of Dora Maar, sculptures in plaster or from readymade objects, and wrote burlesque plays. The Occupation is, of course, a murky period, and there are examples of Picasso acting with great courage in support of friends, or with great cowardice. Most painfully, he refused to help Max Jacob, who was arrested in 1944 and died in the notorious deportation camp of Drancy before Cocteau's efforts to help him could come to fruition. The year 1944 was important for Picasso. He hosted a reading of his own play *Desire Caught by the Tail* by a cast including Jean-Paul Sartre, Simone de Beauvoir and Michel Leiris. After the liberation of Paris, Picasso announced that he had joined the Communist Party, a political affiliation that he maintained to the end of his life. The day after this announcement, the Autumn Salon opened a Picasso retrospective, one so ridiculed by reactionary art students and anti-communists that police had to provide security.

Picasso had met Françoise Gilot in 1943, and began to make paintings of her in 1944, though he also had an affair with a student, Geneviève Laporte, that year. His relationships with Dora Maar and Françoise ran in tandem for a while. After completing the monumental painting commemorating the holocaust, *The Charnel House*, in May 1945, Picasso set off for Antibes with Dora while renting a room nearby for Françoise that she didn't occupy. Picasso then bought a house for Dora at Ménerbes by way of a settlement. Picasso and Françoise were living together by April 1946 and before long she became pregnant with a son, Claude, born in May 1947. During the pregnancy Picasso was given carte blanche to work in the Antibes museum, a castle on the sea with vast rooms, where he painted scenes of Mediterranean idylls and animal subjects on plywood. The year 1947 also saw Picasso take up ceramics enthusiastically, working at the Madoura Pottery in Vallauris. The following year Picasso, Françoise and Claude moved to a villa nearby called La Galloise, where in 1949 Françoise gave birth to a daughter, Paloma ("Dove"), named perhaps after the ceramic doves Picasso had been making.

Picasso made brilliant animal sculptures in this period out of found objects, but he also tried to respond to world events and his communist loyalties with the painting *Massacre in Korea* (1951), and in the following year he made the panel paintings *War and Peace* for a disused chapel in Vallauris. When Stalin died in 1953, Picasso made a portrait of him that was unpopular with Communist Party officials. This led to a cooling of Picasso's communist enthusiasms. During 1953 Picasso and Françoise also became estranged, but at Madoura the following year Picasso met Jacqueline Roque, who soon settled with him first in Paris and then in 1955 in a new villa, La Californie, above the bay at Cannes. In 1958 he bought the quieter Château de Vauvenargues near Aix-en-Provence.

During his years with Françoise, Picasso had been the subject of a large number of important exhibitions in Europe and the USA, and monographs on aspects of his work began to be published regularly, while his private life became of interest to photographers and

journalists. In 1957 he was commissioned to paint
a mural for the new UNESCO building in Paris, and
to produce concrete sculptures for a government
building in Oslo, but he also set himself the challenge
of painting variations on Velázquez's *Las Meninas*.
These were among a series of variations in Picasso's
last years that reflected his ambition to outdo work
by some of the greatest painters in European art
(Delacroix, Poussin, Manet). Many of his fellow
moderns had died (Matisse in 1954, Braque and
Cocteau in 1963). In 1968 the *Las Meninas* variations
were donated to what became the Museu Picasso
in Barcelona in memory of Picasso's old friend and
secretary, Jaime Sabartés, who died that year.

Picasso's first wife Olga Khokhlova died in 1955,
and in 1961 he decided to marry Jacqueline, who
remained possessively devoted to him for the rest
of his life. That same year Picasso moved again
to the grand farmhouse Notre-Dame-de-Vie near
Mougins, partly to be close to the printmakers Aldo
and Piero Crommelynck with whom he began an
intense collaboration in 1963. Apart from a period of
convalescence after an operation in 1965, Picasso's
remaining years saw a burst of activity in printmaking,
sculpture and painting. The paintings, shown in two
major exhibitions at the Palais des Papes, Avignon, in

1970 and 1973, were controversial for their perceived lack of control, leading some to see signs of decline, though they were rediscovered by a new generation of artists and dealers in the 1980s. Picasso died intestate on April 8, 1973, aged 92, a few months before the second Avignon exhibition opened. He was buried in the garden of the Château de Vauvenargues. A protracted legal negotiation between his legitimate and illegitimate heirs led eventually to a large donation to the French state of works from his personal collection which toured many cities before becoming the core of the Musée Picasso in Paris.

Q&A

NOW LET'S START TALKING ...

Over the following pages, Picasso engages in
an imaginary conversation covering ten themes,
responding freely to searching questions.

The questions are in italic type;
Picasso's answers are in roman type.

DEATH –
AND LIFE

Picasso was notoriously superstitious about anything to do with death, an aspect of his character perhaps influenced by his early life in Spain and his experience of family tragedy. During his youthful adventures as an artist in Barcelona and Paris he witnessed urban poverty and disease, and he knew several artists who committed suicide. It is out of these distressing experiences that features of Picasso's early art appear to develop, though the question remains as to how much weight should be given to the life in interpreting the work. Picasso himself was keenly interested in this question.

Señor Picasso, thank you for agreeing to see me and discuss your remarkable life in art. May we begin with your earliest works? You started with portraits, landscapes and pictures of animals. But it's notable that your first successes were with paintings of suffering, illness and death – I'm thinking of Last Moments, *a picture you later painted over, which was shown in the Universal Exhibition in Paris in 1900. And then all those Blue Period paintings of addicts and starving beggars.*

Death is everywhere in Spanish festivals and the Catholic Church, and in those days people used to get executed in public, which is horrible. I hate the Church – though Jacqueline my wife says I am more Catholic than the pope! I have come into close contact with death at times in my life, like everyone else. I lost my beautiful sister Conchita when I was only thirteen or fourteen. Then in 1901 my friend Carles Casagemas shot himself while I was back in Spain – he didn't do a very good job, a bit like Van Gogh. I felt bad that I hadn't been there to stop him making a fool of himself over a woman – that's what caused it all. So I made a picture of him on his deathbed, with a Van Gogh background and candle – a bit too sentimental. Then I made a

much better picture that I suppose you could
say is about art, death and love, which is called
Life. I painted it over *Last Moments*, the picture
you mentioned: it was a good decision!

*Was it the suicide of Casagemas that prompted all
those sombre Blue Period paintings?*

Well, perhaps it was in my mind – but there were
many other things that affected me, and my palette
changed at the same time as my subjects changed.
I was poor then, and I felt sympathy for the poor,
so I wanted to paint them. And I admired the
work of illustrators like Steinlen, who drew poor
people. I'll never forget the prostitutes I saw in the
prison at St Lazare – their despair, their miserable
diseases. These things become a part of one's art
somehow.

Did you ever contemplate suicide in those early years?

No, never. Look, I don't like death and have never
sought it out. I am working against it all the time –
I want to defeat it. That's why I don't go to funerals
if I can help it. They give me the creeps … being
around death is bad luck.

*Looking across your career, many art historians have
also seen memento mori or elegies to recently deceased
friends in your still-life paintings.*

Art historians! Critics! What do they know? When
I paint a skull, it's just that: a skull. Sure, when I
did that in 1908 it was after the German painter
Wiegels hanged himself – drug addiction did for him
– in the Bateau-Lavoir, but I didn't set out to make
a tombstone. This skull was connected to seeing
Wiegels hanging there, the shock. But I don't set out
to make my art based on themes or stories – things
just come to me as I work. Even with *Life*, which is,
I suppose, an exception, the picture just evolved
– it just became a story about human desires and
suffering as I worked. An apple becomes a pear; a jug
becomes a skull. And then the critic sees a memorial
to Wiegels, or Julio González, or Max Jacob or
someone. But what does it mean to see a painting
as a memorial? People always want pictures to have
an answer. We should just be satisfied with looking
– with seeing that a picture is right, and is what the
artist intended.

*I'm not sure I fully understand. Are you saying that
your work, or at least your work when it's finished,*

is almost always nothing to do with what's happened in your life?

No, what I'm saying is that my life is my work. They are the same thing! I could even say that I live my work – you can find more of me there than in the story of my daily routines or my love life or whatever you wish. I have often said that my work is like a diary, but by this I don't mean to say that you can just work out why I painted a fish one day by asking the maid what she cooked for me! Or that you can deduce that I hated a lover because I painted her nose a certain way. As I told my friend Brassai, I used to dream of a future "science of man" that will be able to study my art and find in it the truth of human existence, the true drama of mankind through the experience of one individual. Again, I say that my work is more than a trace of my life, or its imprint, it is my life. As such, it is a complicated thing that is also much more simple than you are making it.

Aren't you trying to make your work more mysterious than it really is, by pretending that your art cannot be decoded in relation to your biography?

Artists have always been misunderstood. That is our fate.

I don't mean to offend – please forgive me! May I come back tomorrow?

Do as you wish – but I may be busy.

POETRY
AND ART

Although we know Picasso as a visual artist in a wide range of media, it is less widely known that for a time he also wrote poetry. In part, this practice reflects his personal friendships with many poets over the course of his life, and his love of certain classics in both Spanish and French literature. More importantly, Picasso's love of visual metaphor (making a flower stand for a woman, for example) is fundamentally poetic in nature. His poetry resembles the stream-of-consciousness writing of James Joyce; its jarring juxtapositions of foodstuffs, creatures and nightmarish visions are also strongly influenced by the dream world of 1930s Surrealism.

*Don Pablo, throughout your life you have been a
particularly close friend of poets and writers – can
you explain why that is?*

When I first got serious about art – I mean when
I got over trying to be an academic artist doing
drawings and paintings in the style admired by my
father in the last days of the 19th century – I used
to hang around a café called Els Quatre Gats in
Barcelona. I got friendly with one or two people who
used to write for a magazine that we published of
the same name. I don't know why it is that I was
drawn to Jaime Sabartés, a poet who in the 1930s
became my secretary and still is, nor why I get on so
well with writers and intellectuals – other than to say
I love books and those who make them. Words must
be made to sing, not merely to chatter. Oh, and of
course Sabartés has an oddly pointed nose: perfect
for caricature!

*Yes, I've seen your portraits of him! But, getting back
to poetry, you don't really have very much time to read,
do you?*

That's true, for I'm always working. Perhaps
knowing poets has been my way of reading! In

1901 when I began to think of making my way in
Paris as an artist, I got to know some poets who
really impressed me, and who made French literature
come alive for me, and also showed me where to find
the real life in Paris. So for a while I was really close
to the Jewish poet Max Jacob whom I met in June
1901. Max read Paul Verlaine and Alfred de Vigny
to me when I was trying to learn French, and those
slow, strong sounds moved me so! Through Max I
discovered Stendhal's thoughts on love – the kind of
thing that preoccupied me in those days! In my first
Paris studio Max and I shared a bed – not together!
– but we slept in shifts, he when I worked, and vice
versa. Max took me to the theatre and the opera,
but things really got going when our little gang was
joined by two other poets: Guillaume Apollinaire
and André Salmon.

*Apollinaire was incredibly important for your career,
wasn't he?*

Yes and no. In 1905 he published some reviews of
my work that got one or two people in the know
talking, but I think that it was really down to others
that I succeeded in the end. I did get to meet lots of
other writers through Apollinaire. Later on he wrote

one or two great things about Cubism, about what
I did with Braque. Sometimes his criticism ended
up talking about stuff that we never believed in
and that belonged in the pretentious artists' cafés –
the "Fourth Dimension" and suchlike. But I loved
Apollinaire, and I always felt so good in his company.
I still miss him. I took a photograph of him in my
studio in 1911 that I still have, sitting next to an
Oceanic sculpture called a *tiki*. And I made lots of
portraits and caricatures of him. He was always
larger than life: the identity of his father was a
mystery, and he encouraged the rumour that it
might even be the pope.

We had endless fun in those days, mocking
everybody and bantering. It was really out of this
banter that my big picture of 1907, *Les Demoiselles
d'Avignon* was first of all called *The Philosophical
Brothel*, and we used to joke that one prostitute in the
picture was Max's grandmother, another Apollinaire's
girlfriend and all that kind of thing. The next minute
we'd be arguing about what modern painting should
be, or who was the greatest French author. In the
evenings we used to go out together to shows that the
ordinary workers in Paris enjoyed – circus performers,
puppet shows, horror stories, gypsy singers. We'd all
shout, laugh and drink too much.

Do you like the poems that Apollinaire wrote about your works?

Of course! This is the best kind of comment on one's art that there can ever be! Apollinaire sent me hand-written drafts of those first poems, "Spectacle" and "Les Saltimbanques", and I still treasure those letters. I wanted to make my own tribute to Apollinaire, a very public one in the form of a monument, but that proved to be very difficult to do for all sorts of stupid reasons. You know, other poets have also set off from my work, most of all my friend Paul Eluard, who published a whole book called *To Pablo Picasso* in 1944. Eluard's poem *End of a Monster* captures for me the tragic moment when the Minotaur – a monster like me! – must face the truth, a moment I thought of often in the worst times of my life.

Do you think that you have learned a lot from poets, then? Have they influenced your choice of subjects in your art, or convinced you of the importance of certain things?

I'm not usually conscious of having done that. For sure I've often been asked to illustrate the work of poets, or to provide something I've already done as an illustration. But there's some truth in what you say, because I've often spoken with those poets I call friends when I've wanted to resolve a problem that bothers me. Michel Leiris has always helped me to see the way forward: this is because he understands that art is a battle – a bullfight – sometimes with demons and sometimes with other artists. It is ridiculous like a bullfight with all that stupid music and those gaudy costumes, but the stakes for a real painter are just as dangerous. I got to know Leiris in the 1920s, when Surrealism was the order of the day among the radical poets and writers. But unlike others in that group, Leiris understands what artists do and the world they exist in, for he is married to Kahnweiler's niece (we all call her Zette), who later on became my most important dealer. The other thing about Leiris is that he is an ethnographer, and he knows all about tribal art. We often talk about the latest African or Oceanic mask I've bought, but not to praise its beauty – we discuss its powerful magic and its dirty, dusty smell! I worry about Leiris sometimes – he has tried to kill himself on several occasions. He understands that art and life are one.

Surrealism inspired you to become a poet yourself, didn't it? I think André Breton, the leader of the group, wrote an article about your poetry in 1935?

When I wrote all those poems, or stories, they came straight to me in a frightening rush. In this way they resemble surrealist texts, those ones that they said were "automatic", though I don't believe in all that. I don't know whether they owe their style to Surrealism or not. For me it was not a question of style or even of deciding to write poetry at all. I was very low just then. It was bad enough when Olga left me and it all came out with Dora about Marie-Thérèse, but even worse when I couldn't paint, I couldn't make sculpture, and I couldn't really draw. I was lost! I'd started to write words down in my sketchbooks, and before I knew it there were hundreds of these "poems".

Did this do anything to help you to return to painting?

In the end, yes, because I began to see how things could mean something again, and how they were always becoming another thing. I used this idea in my poem that went with my protest prints *Dream and Lie of Franco* in 1937, a poem about the way that cries of suffering bring all things in the world to tears.

What's your own view of Surrealism?

It was one of those movements that are made for artists who need to belong to a church. That's why they called Breton the "Pope of Surrealism"! I didn't want to be in that church, but I agreed with a lot of what the surrealists stood for. I, too, believe that art expresses our desires, that art is a weapon in a war against war, that Negro art is better than Raphael, and that art speaks out for "mad" love. I too am a communist. But neither Dalí's dreams nor Miró's improvisations have anything in common with my paintings.

CREATING
CUBISM

Perhaps Picasso's greatest feat as an artist was the invention of a new idiom, Cubism, in partnership with Georges Braque. This collaboration, which flourished in the years 1908–1914 but had a lasting effect on both artists, also had enormous impact internationally. Cubism saw a sea-change in ideas of spatial representation, and a revolution in sculpture. Until 1912, cubist paintings, mostly still lifes or figures, are almost monochrome. Notwithstanding the almost mocking name "Cubism", they are made up of intersecting lines and shading rather than cubes. Later on, colour was reintroduced, and space and form were conjured up in overlapping planes, often made of paper or other foreign materials.

Good afternoon, Don Pablo. It is wonderful to see your Still Life with Chair Caning *on the wall over there, from 1912. Are you still proud of it?*

Of course! When I look at these things, cubist collages, pasted papers, little cardboard sculptures, I see such marvellous techniques that I wonder why I ever went back to oils.

Can you tell me a little about how you discovered Cubism with Georges Braque?

The first thing to say is that Braque and I did not know what we were doing! When you say we "discovered Cubism", it sounds like it was an uncharted island waiting for us to set foot on it. But it wasn't like that at all. Nobody knew what it was we were doing. Later, when people started trying to explain it – and that was already happening by 1910 – they made up all sorts of rubbish about the "Fourth Dimension" and analysis and things. But these were just theories – one might as well listen to the birds.

Centuries of work by thousands of artists led up to Cubism, and it needed slow and painstaking effort by Braque and me to get back to zero and make a new kind of art. I met Braque in 1907, I think, but

really got to know him in 1908 after I had seen his
exhibition at Kahnweiler's that November – amazing
pictures of L'Estaque that made space solid in a
way I found exhilarating. In fact, Braque had seen
my *Demoiselles* and tried to make his own cubist
woman. So I think it's impossible to say whether he
or I invented this art – we were mountaineers roped
together then. Braque was devoted to Cézanne. This
was nothing special, as many artists were working
with Cézanne's ideas, especially after his death in
1906, but Braque plumbed the depths of his art by
holding on to every trace of his anxiety. Cézanne's
anxiety – that's what interested us. And this anxiety is
what made Cézanne hold in his gaze a leaf, so that he
could have the branch, the tree, the whole landscape.

You and Braque had very different temperaments, I think.
Is this why your partnership worked?

Yes. He was my wife! I worked much faster than he
did. Braque was methodical, a thinker and an artisan
combined. I think he got this artisan thing from
his father, who was a painter and decorator. I made
four canvases for every one that Braque made. And
I have always seen my art as about things and people
– everything in my art is someone or something I

know that terrifies or bewitches me. So all my art is
metamorphosis. But Braque, he is a peasant like the
Le Nain brothers, an artisan like Chardin, moving a
tobacco pipe a little to the left, or a coffee cup a little
to the right, balancing things and perfecting them.
This is why I think Braque got closer to abstract art
than I ever did.

*Is that really true? Surely your cubist heads of around
1913 are more abstract than things that Braque did?*

No, not at all. My heads are always heads! Braque was
interested in form for its own sake. I think you can see
this in his later work – those *Studio* paintings that he
did in the 1940s. Douglas Cooper has one, but I don't
think it is interesting and I don't understand it.

*Can we come back to the story of your discovery – I mean
invention – of Cubism. What happened when you saw
Braque's L'Estaque paintings at Kahnweiler's?*

Well, I thought, he has learned a lot from my nudes
and still lifes! And I wanted to see what I could do
with this strange space – everything looking like it
had been under a steamroller and flattened out in
bizarre ways. Yet at the same time Braque's pictures

were full of three-dimensional space. So when I
went off to Horta the following year, I did all sorts
of things to make every aspect of things appear on
the two-dimensional canvas. This was when I made
a kind of crazy move – I made a cubist sculpture
of Fernande's head. I turned the two-dimensional
interpretation of space back into three dimensions!
I made a cubist apple too – I gave the real apple that
I copied to the Czech collector Kramářr. Cubist
painting really got going in 1910, when Braque and
I started taking everything apart in painting: shadows,
lines, spaces. We abandoned colour. We made
pictures out of lines and dabs of paint that were as
grand as Corot.

*So, was the two-dimensional interpretation of three-
dimensional objects the most important idea for you in
those days?*

Look, if I say "yes" you will think that you have
understood Cubism – and that would be an error! As
I said, even Braque and I did not understand it. And in
any case, that wouldn't explain a lot of the things we
did, like putting newspaper lettering on our canvases,
or sticking real things on the canvas – like that printed
chair-caning pattern on the still life over there. These

things happened between Braque and me – they were jokes, and they were very serious too. I put the chair caning on my painting, and framed it with a real piece of rope in May 1912. In September 1912 Braque stuck imitation wood-grain paper down on some drawings. But then I made my *Guitar* out of cardboard! And so it went on.

A lot of other artists became cubists, didn't they? What did you think of them?

Some others made interesting works – Gris was a talent, and he even made his name with a painting called *Homage to Picasso*! Léger went on to do great things. But there were a lot of painters who were better at talking than painting – Metzinger, whom I knew a bit, wasted his ability. But Lhote, Gleizes, Le Fauconnier and the rest are forgotten. All this parade in the Salons made Braque and me retreat further and spurred us to find more revolutionary means. Kahnweiler, who by then, I mean by 1911 or so, was our dealer, also discouraged us from showing our work with these youngsters who called themselves cubists.

Kahnweiler was very important to you? As was Vollard?

We were lucky to have Kahnweiler, and he remained
a friend. Vollard, too, was decent enough, and
like Kahnweiler had an eye. Flechtheim and Level
were reliable, honest. But you know, I don't trust
dealers in the end – I had the worst times with
them when I had no money in my first years in Paris.
Then, when my mother made the mistake of giving
away my childhood works to liars in 1930, I really
saw them for what they are – vultures! Kahnweiler
made a lot of connections outside France – he sold
things to Germans, Russians, Czechs, Americans.
And those people got a lot of my best cubist things.
In fact, I still sell work through Kahnweiler's niece
Zette Leiris.

You know, when I talk about the cubist days
I always feel nostalgic. I think that in Cubism we
discovered the heroism of ordinary things – cigarette
packets, a glass of wine – the ordinary things of the
city. These things were for a while more important
than our personalities as artists – and we tried
to get away from ourselves and be like workmen,
anonymous. That's why we didn't sign our works
on the front for a while. But, of course, this couldn't
last, and our works became different according to
our own personalities.

Why do you think this happened? Why do you think that the Cubism that you and Braque had invented could not continue?

I don't know. I once said that I put Braque on the train at Avignon in his uniform to go off to the Front, and that I never saw him again. What I meant was that we couldn't go back to those times, to how things were before the war when we made sculptures out of tin, wood and cardboard and believed we were making a new art. It's ridiculous that we had to give this up. I do see Braque occasionally, but it's not the same. I've gone on using Cubism, of course. I treat space according to the needs of the painting – I resist all that crowd-pleasing charm in the museums that is badly painted anyway – Rubens, Veronese, all that nonsense. But what Cubism really was when Braque and I worked together, that is impossible these days!

THE
ALL-ROUND
ARTIST

A prolific painter and draughtsman, Picasso also produced huge numbers of prints, sculptures, ceramics as well as photographs and even jewellery. The circumstances behind these different activities that he undertook throughout his life are diverse, and each involved a different kind of interaction with technicians and specialists. But mercurial as his range of activity was, the images and objects produced remain unmistakably Picassian and seem nearly always to exist in some kind of dialogue with painting. Though he sometimes stopped painting to occupy himself with everything from prints to poems, Picasso always returned to it.

*I've recently seen some of your sculptures in sheet metal.
How did that come about?*

It's a funny story. I was eating in a restaurant in
Golfe-Juan in 1946 with Françoise. It was empty but
for two men at another table. I had the feeling they
were keen to talk to me and they seemed to know
who I was, so we got chatting. I was bothered that
day because I had this pet owl I'd adopted when it
turned up in my studio, but I had to go back to Paris.
One of the men, Lionel Prejger, offered to look after
it. I forgot about all this, but then Prejger delivered
the owl to my Paris studio a couple of years later
when I was out. He came up to me again in the same
Golfe-Juan restaurant in 1948 and told me who he
was. I found out that he ran all sorts of scrap metal
and manufacturing businesses. It was only in 1960
that I visited his factory and got interested in working
with a brilliant craftsman there, Tiola. I designed a
toy horse for my grandson Bernard, and Tiola made
it for me out of steel tubing. After that he made lots
of sheet metal sculptures for me, which I love.

In what form did you pass your designs on to Tiola?

I made little cardboard models. It was really

wonderful – like re-doing my cardboard sculptures from cubist times.

Doing the sheet metal sculptures is just one example of a lot of collaborations you've had with craftsmen and technicians, isn't it?

Yes. It's a privilege to work with those who love their craft. I first did complicated metal sculptures with my friend Julio González, who welded steel wires together based on my drawings. I got to know González around 1900 – and in fact it was his brother Joan who gave me the zinc plate on which I did my first etching, *The Frugal Repast*. But we fell out, and then Joan died. I didn't get back in touch with Julio until the early '20s, and we started working together on a monument to Apollinaire. It was a trial because of the people involved in the commission – but working on it in González's studio made me feel as happy as I was in 1912 when I made my metal guitar. In the early 1930s we made some sculptures together that I adore: *Head of a Woman* and *Woman in a Garden*.

And what about your collaborations with printmakers and with ceramicists?

Well, I bought a small press in 1907. And I made some cubist etchings for a book by Max Jacob. But really I didn't get into printmaking seriously until the late 1920s, when I did some etchings of an artist at work that Vollard later published as illustrations to Balzac's *The Unknown Masterpiece*. When the publisher Albert Skira asked me to illustrate Ovid, I wasn't keen at first. I used the printmaker Louis Fort, but it wasn't much of collaboration. Things were different when I did the *Vollard Suite* with Roger Lacourière. He was a brilliant man: he taught me how much you can do with aquatint. It was also at his atelier much later that I met his young assistant Aldo Crommelynck, a man of great skill, with whom I work now.

Lacourière said that he loved your enthusiasm for the medium, and the way you always wanted to do new things in printmaking. Is innovation the most important thing for you when you work in a new medium?

It's true that I always look for the accident, for the chance mistake that opens new doors. That's because I believe that really there are no accidents – just revelations of ourselves. So I made Rembrandt's face out of a mistake, cracked varnish, and I always tried to mix different printing methods to achieve drama.

But you see, when you're working with a printer who knows his onions, you get inspired all the time to surprise him, to beat him at his own game! Anyway, I had my own press in Boisgeloup, and I used to try out all sorts of funny ideas – adding suet and nail varnish. My own prints were always rough – but the prints that Lacourière, his successor Frélaut, or Aldo did from my plates are always wonderful. I look at the proofs carefully now, and if things are not right I do more work or ask for a change in the printing process. I have done lithographs with Mourlot and linocuts with Arnéra.

Yes, Mourlot said that you listened patiently to everything he taught you – and then ignored it. Can you talk a little about the ceramics you've done, and how you got involved in that?

Ceramics – you should try it! It's magnificent! I made some ceramics way back in the early years with Paco Durrio, a friend of Gauguin, and a couple of nice pots in the late '20s with Jean van Dongen's help. But really I only got into it in 1947, when I started working at the Madoura Pottery run by the Ramiés in Vallauris. That's where I really learned about glazes and kiln temperatures and all that stuff – it's a process that makes you settle on everything once and for all, and then there's the risk, the firing, when the pot can crack or turn out badly. Jules Agard used to throw forms for me on the wheel, and then I would grab them and shape them. That's how I made the famous dove – by taking a pot and wringing its neck! Other times I used crocks and bits of kiln furniture and made things out of them. I also did a lot of plates where I just painted a design on them – tricks on the eye showing bullfight scenes in perspective.

What do you feel about your decision to allow the Ramiés to make replicas, editions of your ceramics? I think some people feel that these are very inferior to your own autograph originals, and that they undermine them.

I don't agree. Of course, a copy is not a Picasso – it doesn't have life in the same way since I didn't imbue it with my feelings through my fingertips. I wanted to thank the Ramiés for their hospitality, and I knew this would set them up. But I think it's important that people can buy these pieces and enjoy my idea – and I hope that they eat their fish off one of my plates every Friday!

*So far we've been talking about various collaborations
– and I think there have been a lot more that we haven't
discussed. But I wanted to ask you about the relationship
between all these collaborations and the more lonely
activity of painting – which do you prefer and why?*

I don't think I have a choice. Painting is stronger
than I am – it makes me do what it wants. When I'm
painting, I don't want to be interrupted, and I don't
want to talk about it with others. Making ceramics
or prints means talking and joking around. Painting
is more serious.

*When you talk about yourself as an artist, you tend to call
yourself a painter. Are you a painter and not, for example,
a sculptor? You've made a great many sculptures, and some
see much of your painting as sculptural.*

I am a painter – but you know, sculpture is the best
comment that a painter can make on painting.

THE IMPORTANCE OF "THINGS"

Some of Picasso's paintings and sculptures incorporate "real" objects, and much of his work focuses on the genre of still life. This interest in making art out of ordinary things extended to Picasso's behaviour, for he amassed an enormous collection of largely worthless material over the course of his life. Some of this hoard of found objects and other items of all kinds followed him around his various houses, while some got left behind as he moved from one place to another.

Don Pablo, it's just wonderful to sit here with you surrounded by all these things that you made, and also by your collection of ... well, what shall I call them ...? Curiosities.

Yes, I love all these things – all this rubbish – and this is just a little sample of my collection of objects. I have rooms full of them all over the place! I'm the King of the Ragpickers!

It looks as if many of the objects on the mantelpiece and on the floor haven't been moved for a while and other things have been piled on top of them.

I know where everything is! And I absolutely hate it when someone tries to tidy my things or dust them. I refuse to have a cleaning lady near my things. Dust is the best friend of a painter! I remember writing to Braque in 1912 and telling him that I was using our latest papery and powdery techniques, and that I'd thrown in a bit of dust as well when I was working on a guitar painting. I wanted to insult the art collectors! I was very proud to have found a role for dust in my art, or for sawdust at least. I used to mix sawdust with my paint to turn it into coarse mud – so beautiful and nasty at the same time.

Is this the Glass of Absinthe, *the sculpture from 1914?*
It's much smaller than I thought, though I guess I should
have known it was, from the real spoon stuck in the top.

Yes, it is one of only six that were cast in bronze –
but I painted each one according to my whim in
different ways, so really they are unique. Most have
coloured dots like a bad Signac, and one is a sad
little thing covered in brown paint and sand. I made
the original in plaster and incorporated the absinthe
spoon at a jaunty angle like a kind of hat.

Was it a very daring thing to do then, to add a real object
to a sculpture?

We weren't afraid to do anything! Apollinaire wrote
some wonderful things about me around 1913,
about how painting could be anything now – pipes,
starched collars, candelabras. Candelabras! You can
see how he influenced me when you look at the *Glass*
of Absinthe. It is like the statue of a saint in a Spanish
procession, those polychromed marvels with a real
hat or hair. I'd put real things in paintings before I put
them in sculptures. No one had done anything like
that in sculpture, except maybe Degas in that crazy
little girl dancer he made with the tutu.

*Did they have an impact on people then, these new kinds
of sculpture?*

Vladimir Tatlin came to my studio and was amazed
– he went back to Russia and invented Constructivism
as a result! I think a lot of modern sculpture comes out
of things like my *Glass of Absinthe*, and my cardboard
and metal *Guitars*. But it is funny how these things
spread – Apollinaire put a few photographs of them
in a magazine in 1913, but they weren't seen by a lot
of people otherwise.

*Surely Marcel Duchamp's readymades in 1915 or so were
inspired by your use of real objects?*

Probably. But I didn't know him at all, and I don't
know what he had seen of my art before 1915. I don't
believe that it is enough just to show an object – you
have to make a new metaphor out of it, one that
convinces. That way, I make you see reality afresh
because there is a movement back and forth between
ordinary things and the metaphors I make of them.

*You had a lot of fun with sculptures of animals in the
1940s and 1950s, where you used found objects to depict
the forms of udders, heads, beaks or whatever.*

Animals have always been around, and somehow
there were more animals around me then than before.
I had a pet goat and a pet owl. But it was also fun
to make animal sculptures for my children, Claude
and Paloma, and to show off to them by reinventing
things that way. I used two of Claude's toy cars to
make the head of a baboon – though I'm not sure he
was pleased!

*Was it in the same spirit that you used a bicycle saddle
and handlebars to make your famous 1942* Head of a
Bull *sculpture?*

Not exactly. This sculpture – you see it high above the
door there – is very important to me for three reasons:
first, it's one of my favourite expressions of my Spanish
background; second, it's a real metaphor, a complete
reinvention of the meaning of the objects I found
dumped in the street; third, you can imagine someone
finding it one day and saying, "This bull's head would
make a great bicycle saddle and handlebars" – and as
I've often said, this would be a real act of creation!
I made it during the Nazi occupation of Paris, when
everything was dark and desperate, when people
had nothing decent to eat and no hope. Rubbish on
the streets is the stuff of art in such times.

I'd like to read you something you said in 1935: "It is my misfortune – and probably my delight – to use things as my passions tell me ... I put all the things I like into my pictures. The things – so much the worse for them; they just have to put up with it." What did you mean, and how does this relate to your sculptures that use real objects?

A lot of things around me excite my feelings, and my feelings colour them, mutate them, and they become part of my life. I grab things – I don't contemplate them like Cézanne or Matisse. And all the things I grab are in my imagination signs for other things. I don't care for anything about them but what they say in my art. This thing over here, for example, is a gas burner from a stove that I just took and upended, because I saw in it a powerful sign for a woman. It is called the *Venus of Gas*, and it's a kind of modern cult object. I think of it as the sort of thing that might be found in a thousand years and interpreted by very serious archaeologists as a clue to the beliefs of 20th-century man. That replica over there of the *Venus of Lespugue* – something some caveman carved 25,000 years ago – is just his sign for woman, like my Venus. Here, lift her up.

She's heavy! Old ironware. So this Venus of Gas *is a true readymade, and that makes it very unusual in your work. But there are all kinds of other things around us that we haven't talked about: skulls, cigarette packets, pieces of wood and pebbles.*

Skulls are beautiful sculptures – bones show the traces of the creator's hand, smoothing here and squeezing the clay of life there, as in the frayed edges of an eye-socket. When I paint a still life or make a sculpture, I always have in mind the sensations of touching things, feeling their roughness or smoothness, as well as how they look. Turning a pebble in my hand reminds me that the things I use have a life of their own.

STYLE VERSUS TECHNIQUE

A word often used to describe Picasso's art is "protean", changing as it does from style to style in a dazzling display of virtuosity seen as proof of his genius. Conversely, some believe that his restless inventiveness was a smokescreen to conceal a lack of depth. Picasso certainly encouraged the view that he was master of a multitude of different manners in art by producing his own versions of the work of artists from many different eras. But when cornered, he also denied that these changes of style were ever made for their own sake.

Excusez-moi, Don Pablo. I didn't know you were on the telephone!

Don't worry. *(Picasso beckons me in, saying to his caller: "I have a visitor, but yes, that sounds marvellous. Why don't you call back when I've thought about it? Goodbye.").* Sit down, sit down. That was Penrose – he's an old friend who has bought some of my works, but he also wrote a biography of my life. He wants to do a translation of my play *The Four Little Girls*. But I really get fed up with all these requests – I want to do my work!

I suppose that Monsieur Sabartés looks after a lot of the calls and letters?

Yes, he does. But, of course, everyone always wants to see me or speak to me on the telephone. Often I avoid it. Today Douglas Cooper is coming for lunch – a fat Englishman who is very rich and buys my work. He wants something, but there will be a lot of other people here as well so I might avoid him. So I don't have very long – what do you want to ask me today?

Well, I'm fascinated by the constant changes of style in your work. I mean the way you've gone from Post-

*Impressionism to Blue and Rose Periods, to Cubism, to
Neo-Classicism, to Surrealism and so on. Why do you
change your style so often?*

These names you give to my painting are just the
invention of dealers and critics. They are not styles
– but in any case I haven't changed styles in my
work because I don't have a style. The trouble with
most painters who have a style is that they just repeat
a formula. Some do this well, like Renoir, but I am
always moving, so as soon as you think you see a
style in my work, I have already changed.

*But there do seem to be occasions when you have
deliberately adopted a style: I'm thinking, for example,
of your use of Neo-Impressionist dots in your portrait
of Olga Khokhlova in 1918, or more notably your
sudden change from Cubism to a classicism influenced
by Ingres around the same time.*

I never understood what all the fuss was about
when I made those portrait drawings in the style
of Ingres in 1915. I think that people can't cope
with an artist unless they can put a label on him.
I have a press cutting somewhere where one
journalist, faced with my portrait of Max Jacob,

asked, "Which is the true Picasso?" Well, the drawing and my cubist *Harlequin* of the same year are both true Picassos. People confuse a change in technique with a loss of nerve, whereas in fact it is the opposite. My classical drawings were very cubist – the proof is that they were better than the classical drawings that I did before Cubism!

If you don't agree with the idea that you change style, could I rephrase the question and ask why do you change technique so often?

I don't have a preconceived idea of a technique that I will use when I make a painting. Or if I do, it never manages to stay the same when I'm painting. If I make a painting of a woman sleeping, I find the manner that suits. Everything in the painting is just a way to express the sleeping woman. Often I change technique several times in the same painting – either different parts of the painting will use different means, or I paint over the scene entirely in a new technique that has come to me just then. I used to say that my painting was not a sum of additions, but a sum of destructions – I destroy what comes first, what is easy, and make a point of destroying beautiful things so that I can find a better expression.

Did you feel that Georges Clouzot's film Le Mystère
Picasso *captured the way your technique changes as
you work?*

Yes, perhaps. Though I didn't like painting in front
of the camera – I was in the bullring and everything
depended on the skill of the toreador! Sometimes
the bull – the canvas – was terrifying. Clouzot
persuaded me to go the premiere of the film in
Cannes in 1956, but I was very nervous and stayed
in bed until the last minute. I wore my dinner
jacket and a bowler hat to cause a stir when I arrived
anyway. Still, I did the film with Clouzot because
it was a new way of understanding the artist's
work – to see it changing and growing before
one's eyes. At the same time some people thought
they could see into my dreams or desires when
they saw the film, and that's stupid – because
even I cannot see them when I look at my own
paintings. Paintings have a life of their own, which
is not mine.

*That's very interesting, but doesn't it contradict your
idea that your work is like a diary? Doesn't your art
always bear a very close relationship to your personal
life?*

That depends what you think it means to write
a diary. We have been talking about my pictures
changing as they are made. Look, even when a
painting of mine is *finished*, it still goes on changing.
Come with me ... now, look at this little painting. It's
of a crucifixion, and I made it in 1930. The women
shriek with grief and Christ is just a sign for a body.
Now, when I made it, I thought of myths and violent
passions. But when I look at it today, I see past these
colours like sour fruits and I think of *Guernica*,
because it's one of the only pictures I made before
1937 that stood for tragedy and chaos. But you will
see something different ... Every thing I do is part of
me, is me. But a lot of what appears does so against
my will. The little sculpture of a cat by the door
– that started as a standing woman, you see? But
then I suddenly saw the woman's breasts as the cat's
muzzle, and I added the body onto the torso and it
just became a cat – I have no idea why! It was the
same when I painted portraits of friends when they
were all down in Mougins in 1937 – I painted Eluard
and made him a woman, an Arlésienne, and then I
ended up exposing his woman's breast and giving him
a cat to feed with his milk! So my diary is a diary of
my thoughts and experiences – but don't look there
for the truth!

I think my time is probably nearly up this morning – but thank you so much for showing me these things.

Well you can come again – I have a lot more things to show you!

THE ART
COLLECTOR

Picasso collected work by other artists from an early date, but the majority of the important works he acquired were purchased later when he had more money at his disposal. The collection, most of it now in the Musée Picasso in Paris, contains some notable works but quite a few indifferent pieces by major artists, and the non-Western objects are also of variable quality. This heterogeneous mix reflects Picasso's egocentric artistic attitude: almost everything in the collection was there to serve his own inspiration.

Don Pablo, we've already talked about the way you hoard many kinds of things. But I wanted to ask you today about your art collection – all the wonderful paintings that you have by other artists.

Well, as I told you, I've never intentionally set about making a collection of anything other than what I like, or what has already been a part of my life. So I suppose that the earliest works I acquired by other artists were by friends. Matisse and I swapped paintings in 1907, just when we got to know each other and discovered how different our approaches were to painting. Matisse was a lot older than I, and very serious in his suits and his spectacles. Anyway, I chose *Marguerite*, a painting of his daughter – let me see if I can find it in this stack … here it is! – and he chose one of my still lifes that was already a bit cubist, showing some lemons and a jug.

Your Matisse has that appealing childlike simplicity, I think.

Yes, Matisse had been studying drawings by his children – that's why the nose is in profile even though the face is seen from the front. That interested me at the time. But Matisse is not simple,

even though it seems that way. I have some other
Matisse works, and an incredibly ugly headdress
figure from Vanuatu that he gave me in the early
1950s not long before he died. It's like a devil,
and I always leave it sitting on an ordinary wooden
chair to scare people!

*You have a few paintings by the naïve artist Henri
Rousseau that are also childlike. How did you get
interested in his work?*

Le Douanier Rousseau! He was a funny type.
I first saw his work in 1901, but I only really got
interested in 1907 when I saw *The Snake Charmer*.
Then I found that painting over there, the one of
the standing woman, in a shop and bought it for
five francs! Back in 1908, in the Bateau-Lavoir days,
we held a banquet in his honour, as if he were being
made a Member of the Legion or something. It was
a bit of a joke, but Rousseau wept tears of joy. After
this he used to visit my studio, and tell me I was
an "Egyptian" painter, whatever that meant. He
used to annoy me, he was foolish and pig-headed,
but he was also a great painter. I bought three more
Rousseaus: a self-portrait, a portrait of his wife,
and a crazy history painting with foreigners coming

to honour the French Republic. Rousseau made everything in his pictures clear and direct, but combined that with fantasy.

What would you say were the most precious paintings in your collection?

You mean the ones I love best? Well, I have two great Cézannes, but the one that I always see in my mind is of five bathers, that one above the sideboard over there. I bought it when I had the money, because I remember seeing Matisse's Cézanne, a picture of three bathers. So I outdid him by getting five! Maybe they match my five women in *Les Demoiselles d'Avignon*, though I see my *Demoiselles* more when I look at my collection of Degas monotypes of prostitutes lounging and touting for clients.

I have a fine Chardin showing a side of mutton, all flesh and blood. I try to match this in my still lifes. There are two Miró portraits and some delicious Renoir nudes. I am making my own Renoirs now, big naked bathers stroking their hair and fondling themselves! I have some other things – Derain, Gauguin, de Chirico – but these are ones that I like to look at often.

*You haven't mentioned Braque. Don't you have anything
by him?*

Yes. I do have a beautiful *Still Life with a Bottle*, from
1911 or so. I am sorry I don't have more. Since Braque
died, I'm the only one left who understands what
passed between us.

*Yes, I'm so sorry that so many of your friends and
fellow painters have gone. But you still look very strong!
What about your collection of non-Western art? Can
you remember which piece you first acquired?*

The first tribal mask I remember seeing in an
artist's studio was a really frightening Fang Mask that
Derain had bought from Vlaminck. Derain thought
it was a beautiful thing, a new kind of sculpture,
and he kept trying to make his own versions in wood
and stone. I didn't see it that way. I started buying
around 1910, I think, and maybe the first things I
had were those wooden figures over there – Leiris
tells me that they are New Caledonian roof post
figures. They were my new Adam and Eve in the
Bateau-Lavoir. I had a *tiki* figure not long after, but
I don't know where it is now, and then that Punu
mask over there by the mirror. I put that mask in

my portrait of Kahnweiler in 1911, like a spirit
watching over him.

*I'm interested that you didn't think Derain's Fang
Mask was beautiful. Is that because you think that all
masks are for exorcism, for warding off evil spirits, as
you told André Malraux in 1937?*

A lot of artists at that time just bought these things
because they wanted to copy them, to find in them
a new image of beauty. But I wanted to do something
to scare the collectors! So for me these tribal things
were a new way of seeing a face, a body that matched
how we imagined those things in our minds, before
all that rubbish about realism got in the way. I thought
African masks were more rational, more conceptual,
than the art in the museums, and they helped me
to re-think the human face in my art. When I spoke
to Malraux, he was asking me about *Les Demoiselles
d'Avignon* and I told him about going to the Trocadéro
Museum in 1907. But I think that it was really only after
my friendship with the surrealists that I could speak of
the masks as talismans or weapons against everything.

*Can you explain why you replied to a survey in 1920 on
African art by saying, "Never heard of it"?*

Maybe I was trying to distance myself from what was fashionable. Back then I think that people saw these carvings as the kind of art that was suitable for decorating apartments or hotel foyers. But I saw it as something that can change the way we see ourselves, a revelation of all the different ways to show a nose or an ear.

I can see a mask here that people have connected to your cubist work: the Grebo Mask, the one with the protruding eyes and mouth.

There *could* be a way that this mask inspired me, because in Cubism, especially the art that Braque and I did later on, after we made collages, we did lots of things in reverse. Shaded things were light, light things were shaded, spaces were solid and solid things became space. In my *Guitar* I made the sound hole in the guitar solid like those eyes on the mask. This was just in the same spirit as the man who made the mask, and who understood that we can make signs for things in many different ways. But I'm not sure that I can remember or know why I did certain things, and there were many different reasons to change everything in our art – to throw out all old ideas – every day.

ART AND
POLITICS

It is only recently, and some years after Picasso's death, that we have learned of his application to become a French citizen in 1940, an application that was turned down as a result of his anarchist and communist sympathies. As a young man Picasso associated with anarchist circles in Barcelona, and in the 1920s became friends with surrealists who were also communist sympathizers, an association that hardened during the Spanish Civil War and the Occupation of Paris. Picasso was one of the most valuable recruits that the French Communist Party ever had, but Party officials found it difficult to accept much of his work.

What a beautiful evening. It was really good of you to invite me.

I'm happy that we can talk after dinner like this – although I need to go back to my studio in an hour or so. I'm working on something that's annoying me, so I must finish it by morning …

Do you always work late?

Yes, normally. I don't like to get up much before midday these days, but then I work until 6 a.m. sometimes. I like to work in artificial light, and find that I prefer the sounds of night-time and the peace in the house. I don't really plan out my work – and on the rare occasions that I've been asked to do something specific to a deadline, I've always found it hard.

Wasn't it like that with your best-known commission, Guernica?

Oh yes, that was really a high-wire act! As you know, I felt very upset by the situation in Spain – I hated Franco, I still hate him and I hate Fascism. I was a Republican. So the Republican Government asked

me to paint a mural for their pavilion in the 1937
World Fair in Paris. It was a beautiful modernist
building by José Luis Sert, and they already knew
the dimensions of the wall I was to paint. But
I couldn't get enthusiastic about it. I did some
drawings of a studio – an artist and a model, one
of my favourite themes ever since the 1920s. But it
was only at the eleventh hour that the bombing of
Guernica happened, and then I knew what I had to
paint. I made the painting in black and white – it
went through changes, and I used coloured paper to
experiment with some ideas. In the end only a little
dark green can be seen and everything else is the
monochrome of those terrible press photos of the
town after the Fascists destroyed it.

The basic idea of the painting came to me
quickly and spontaneously – all my ideas of Spain
as the bullfight came together with the cries of
women and children. It is my protest against
brutality and Fascism.

You also made two sheets of etchings called Dream
and Lie of Franco, *and these were designed to help
the Republicans, weren't they?*

Yes. They are like strip cartoons, with nine images

on each sheet, and originally I thought they would be mass-reproduced as postcards. But in the end they were sold for a lot more as original etchings.

So how did you feel as a Spaniard who had lived so long in France, I mean when the Civil War broke out?

I am a Spaniard and I will die a Spaniard. It was a terrible time for me. A lot of things were going wrong personally too. I was close to Eluard, who had published a poem against the bombings in Madrid in 1936 in the communist paper *L'Humanité*. I published a statement about my painting before *Guernica* was finished where I said that all my work at that time was an expression of my horror at the military dictatorship turning Spain into "an ocean of misery and death". But when *Guernica* was installed – it was after the pavilion had opened – I got a lot of criticism from people on the Left who thought my painting was unclear. I helped the Republicans in other ways: I gave money and I became an honorary director of the Prado as a way to signal my belief in art as opposed to the death cult of Franco and his generals.

What led you to join the Communist Party in 1944?

It was a natural thing for me at the time – I'm
still a member of the Party and I shall be till I die. I'd
always been against poverty, against oppression – I'd
seen the effects of that in my early years in Barcelona,
and I was appalled when the Spanish authorities
executed the anarchist Ferrer in 1909, though I was
never really an anarchist in terms of action. During
the Nazi occupation I had to endure the deaths of
close friends like Jacob and Desnos at the hands of
those bastards and their collaborators. I knew a lot of
Resistance people too. When I joined the Party, I felt
as if I had found a true homeland, since I could not
return to Spain while Franco ruled there. My painting
was in any case always revolutionary in its means,
and I am sure that it shows the colour of the times,
even if I did not, except in *Guernica*, deliberately set
out to make politically engaged art. I made some
paintings after that that were intended to support
communism in its struggle to make men clearer
thinkers, and to fight imperialism. *Massacre in Korea*
was the most important of these, but it wasn't well
received by the Party. Nor was my portrait of Stalin
that Aragon published after the leader's death in
Les Lettres Françaises. It's very difficult to try to make
communist art deliberately – I am a communist so
all my painting is inevitably communist. But if I

were a shoemaker and a communist, I wouldn't hammer shoes a special way to show that I'm a communist.

But would you really say that your paintings of Françoise in that period, the ones that are so serene, or your ceramics and animal sculptures made at this time are communist? How can they be political art?

I once wrote a little note for an American artist – one of the hundreds who besieged me in my studio after the Liberation. If you wait a minute, I can find a book where it's printed ... Here ... read this out while I light another cigarette.

From where? The second paragraph? Okay. "What do you think an artist is? An imbecile who has only eyes if he's a painter, ears if he's a musician, or a lyre in every chamber of his heart if he's a poet, or even, if he's a boxer, only some muscles? Quite the contrary, he is at the same time a political being constantly alert to the horrifying, the passionate or pleasing events of the world, shaping himself completely in their image ... No, painting is not made to decorate apartments. It's an offensive and defensive weapon against the enemy."

Do you understand? Art is the enemy of ignorance and idiocy. It's just that very few governments have the courage to bring in laws against the use of certain colours, or the wrong line ... Now, I must go to my studio and make more war!

CELEBRITY CIRCUS?

In 1965 the British critic John Berger famously castigated Picasso for having failed as an artist in his later life, succumbing to the temptations of fame, clowning around for photographers and visitors, and churning out trivial works with no real subject matter. As a result of the attentions of a large number of talented photographers, Picasso's image soon became a fundamental element of his artistic identity, and this image appeared in popular magazines as well as coffee table books promising intimate glimpses of the artist's world.

Good afternoon Don Pablo. I'm intrigued to see you with all those photographs.

They're by David Douglas Duncan, an American I trust, who's taken a lot of snaps of Jacqueline and myself and sometimes of my studio. I like to have a record of the evolution of a work, and these ones show me working on a portrait of Jacqueline in 1958. Dora Maar did something similar when I painted *Guernica*, but just a series of the picture in different states. Duncan's photos show me too – what do you think?

Well, they seem fascinating, and they show how intensely you concentrate when you work. Do you enjoy being photographed?

Yes, why not? And I like taking photographs too, but I don't do it so much now.

When do you think people became interested in publishing photographs of you? Was it because of Guernica?

Well, lots of people had taken photographs of me before that – when I went to Rome and Naples with Cocteau in 1917, for example. But the first

important photographs I remember being taken
about me were not of me as such, but of my studio
at Boisgeloup by Brassai, a wonderful photographer
and a great friend. These were published in the
surrealist journal *Minotaure* in 1933 (I did the cover
for that first issue), and Breton wrote a text to go
with them. I thought Brassai's photographs were
so superb that they really said something about my
work as a sculptor just then. Photography sometimes
helps me to see my work in new ways. Zervos is
making a catalogue of my paintings and drawings
by photographing them. Early on I used to play with
photographs to make new kinds of works, but now
I don't bother with that.

*Didn't Brassai take a lot of photographs of you in the rue
des Grands Augustins apartment and the Grenier during
the Nazi occupation?*

Yes, but before, during and after the war. My place
then was a kind of rendezvous for a lot of people:
Sartre and de Beauvoir, Leiris and Zette, Camus,
Cocteau and his boyfriend the actor Jean Marais.
Lots of people involved in the Resistance, poets,
intellectuals. Brassai used to come around too, and
he and I used to talk a lot. He published a book about

our conversations a few years ago. Anyway, Brassai took a lot of photographs of things then, especially the sculptures I was making, as well as photos of me with my dog Kasbek, or of gatherings of friends. I think he took some photos of us at the Café de Flore and other restaurants too. Maybe that's when you could say that I started to get photographed for being well known.

Then when I joined the Communist Party in 1944, and became famous – or notorious – for my art at the Salon de la Libération and at other exhibitions, that's when my reputation as a public figure got going. I still have a collection of hate mail from then – someone even smeared some shit on a piece of paper and wrote: "here is some shit from a 60-year old prostitute's arse = your pictures"! When you get letters like that, you know you're in the public eye!

So how did this develop after the war? When was it that you became aware that a lot of photographers were interested in you?

I think it was when I broke up with Dora Maar and my relationship with Françoise got going. Françoise was very photogenic, and we were in love and used to go for a swim down in Antibes where I was working in the Château Grimaldi. Robert Capa took a very clever photograph of me clowning around, holding a parasol over Françoise's head while I walked on the beach. Robert Doisneau took some equally famous pictures – the one where I made some bread rolls look like my fingers, and so on. One ended up on the cover of a special issue of the American magazine *Life*. These photos seem to be very popular, but a lot of other photographers came to me in those days. When I used to hang around in Cannes in the late 1950s or go to the bullfight in Arles, there were always photographers wanting to shoot us, to show me with Cocteau and Jacqueline, or fooling around with Claude. Press photographers like stars and they like a stunt.

Did this annoy you at all? I mean, did you feel that people were becoming more interested in you as a star and less interested in your art?

Yes, it did annoy me, but as much for the constant requests from photographers and journalists to visit the studio as for the way people saw me. I hate being interrupted all the time! To be honest, people can think what they like – I don't care.

Hmmm ... I think you said something to Duncan like,
"fame is the worst thing that can happen to an artist – a
punishment from God".

Did I? Well, I suppose it's true. But maybe it depends
on what we mean by fame, because an artist needs
to live! When Brassai came to my studio on rue La
Boétie in 1932, I was riding high having put together
a big retrospective exhibition in Paris and then
Zurich. I installed the Paris show – but I found it a
chore. Now I think it was a great exhibition because
I didn't do obvious things – I put works together
from different years side by side. But I let the Zurich
museum director install the one there, and he just
put everything in chronological order, which is not
so interesting. I think everyone since then just copied
him, even Barr in New York, who is a clever man ...
What were we talking about?

Fame ...?

Oh yes. Well, these exhibitions in 1932 brought their
fair share of horrible criticism. Ignorance! But for
the dealers and the museums it was part of a process
that meant my work was always in demand, and
so I had money and could do what I wanted. *That*

kind of fame is necessary. I like to live like a pauper
– with lots of money! I used to annoy Olga by
wearing my painting clothes in my chauffeur-driven
Hispano-Suiza!

You mentioned the 1968 Life *double issue on you and your
work. I think that it reproduces quite a few photographs
of you wearing masks and fooling about in capes and the
like. Do you worry that this undermines your credibility
as a serious artist?*

No. I like to play – my art is work but it's also play.
We need enthusiasm more than ever. Matisse was the
serious grand man of art. A great painter, the greatest
painter we had, but he didn't know how to laugh!

LOVE AND FAMILY LIFE

Picasso's irregular private life was the subject of press attention for many decades. Remarkably, he managed a considerable degree of privacy over his liaisons, even keeping long-running affairs from the closest friends. His litigation to prevent various kiss-and-tell memoirs from being published demonstrates how jealously Picasso guarded his privacy, and how much he worried about his reputation not only in public terms but also with current partners. He paid Fernande Olivier a lump sum and pension to suppress some of her memoirs during his lifetime. But Picasso's conduct was not noble, and his former partners had everything to gain and little to lose from exposing some of his personal failings.

Would you mind if we talked today about your family
life? In that Life *magazine special issue you mentioned*
the other day, there's an article about the women with
whom you've been involved: "The wonder is he ever had
time to paint!" is the subtitle.

I suppose it's inevitable that such matters get
discussed. But I detest this obsession with my private
life. Some of these women have wanted revenge
when I left them or when things went bad. Françoise
Gilot published that stupid book about me – I tried to
stop the French edition in 1965 through lawyers but
failed because apparently the fact that there are lies in
it about me was not a good enough reason. She made
me sound like a philosopher half the time, and put
words in my mouth about women that were meant
to make me into an ogre. Fernande Olivier published
some of her memoirs in 1930 in the newspaper
Le Soir, but at least I can say now that what Fernande
said was true. She brought out a whole book in 1933
and we tried to stop that too. But you know, I saw her
on television some years ago and I was upset at the
state she's in these days. Would you like a grape?

No, thank you. I wonder if you have regrets, then, about
your affairs?

It is not my fault that women can't accept things,
or that they think everything you say in bed is
forever! It was Fernande who had the affair, anyway,
that led to our split. And she introduced me to
Eva Gouel whom I really loved but who died only
a few years later. My father died around then too –
it was an awful time. Maybe it was after that that
I really wanted to get married. I was doing well and
wanted to settle down – I felt I was tired of Bohemia.

*So you chose Olga Khokhlova because she was more
conventional?*

Yes. But I didn't choose her first. There were others
around that I was interested in too. But Olga was
part of the Ballet Russes and very beautiful in a
classic way. We had our son Paulo a few years after
we were married, and we knew a lot of sophisticated
people in Paris. It was a new life, with fancy-dress
parties and servants and all that. Summers in chic
resorts. Olga was very particular, and that got on
my nerves because I like things not to be disturbed
by cleaners and maids fussing around.

*You mentioned your son Paulo. Were you happy to be
a father? Do you think that your feelings about*

*fatherhood were a reaction to the death of your father
in 1913?*

I don't know. My father was important to me as a
boy because he was a painter. One day he asked me
to finish one of his paintings of a pigeon, to do the
claws. I did it and that evening he saw that my claws
were better than his pigeon – so he handed me his
brushes! The trouble with my father, though, was
that he was bourgeois through and through. I hated
that about him, and maybe this is why I have always
tried to be Bohemian even when, as in my days with
Olga, I am living as a bourgeois. But, you know, all
the men in my work are really my father! And yes, I
liked being a father, for I love children and their noise
and simple view of things. I was very happy when
Claude and Paloma were kids and we used to play
around together, drawing and play-acting. This is
how life should be.

*Would you say that you had similar feelings about your
mother – ambivalent feelings?*

Not at all. My mother adored me and that is as it
should be. I had to put up with her sometimes, but
there was never really any problem between us –

well, only when she was duped into handing over
hundreds of my earliest works to sharks in 1930.
It took me years of fighting with vermin dealers
and a fortune in legal fees to get them back!

*And while that was going on, things were difficult with
Olga? Wasn't this when you were also seeing Marie-
Thérèse Walter?*

Yes, it's true. But the situation then was very
complicated, and I prefer not to speak about it. What
I can tell you is that Olga was often ill – she suffered
physically and mentally. I had thought of divorce in
order to be with Marie-Thérèse, especially after our
daughter Maya was born in 1935, but, you know, I
didn't want to lose half of everything, so Olga and
I arranged a separation. This was an amazing time in
my life as an artist and as a Spaniard. The Civil War
affected me, and I painted *Guernica* and a lot of other
things that were reactions to the state of affairs. At
the same time I felt that those closest to me were a
part of my imagination – so I felt Olga and Marie-
Thérèse in my pictures too. I deformed Olga in some
of them, and punished her for her rages, trapped her
in stuffed armchairs like a bird in a cage … And then
along came Dora Maar, charming and strong, but

pig-headed. Everyone wants something from me
in the end, everyone except Jacqueline.

*Do you think that each of these women has made you
produce a different kind of art?*

Perhaps. Well, inevitably. But you have to remember
that art is not truth, it is a lie that makes us see
the truth. Truth is in any case a lie. Truth is a lie –
remember it. Of course, some of the paintings I made
of Olga or Dora were just that – portraits of Olga and
Dora. Or my *Woman-Flower*, which is a portrait of
Françoise. At the same time many of my paintings are
exorcisms, so demons appear that are not real people
but the forms that stand for my feelings at the time.

*After all your lovers, Jacqueline is only your second wife,
and you seem to have found true happiness with her.
You've made many portraits of her as far as I can see,
both paintings and sculptures.*

She is everything to me. She makes it possible for
me to work. Now, you see this grape stem – all that
is left of my grapes – it's like my family tree, with
many branches! But underneath there's a pattern,
a force of nature. That is the path of the Minotaur!

FURTHER RESEARCH

GENERAL BOOKS

Tim Hilton's book is still impressive, if dismissive of Picasso after 1945 – a judgment shared with Berger's polemic. Cowling's book stops in 1939, but is a wonderfully lucid journey through Picasso's different visual styles. Though dated, the Penrose/Golding anthology remains an excellent collection of essays.

John Berger, *The Success and Failure of Picasso* (Harmondsworth: Penguin, 1965)

Elizabeth Cowling, *Picasso: Style and Meaning* (London: Phaidon, 2002)

Neil Cox, *Essential Artists: Picasso* (London: Tate Publishing, 2009)

Tim Hilton, *Picasso* (London: Thames and Hudson, 1975)

Roland Penrose and John Golding (eds.), *Picasso in Retrospect* (London: Granada, 1981)

BIOGRAPHIES

There are a large number of biographies available of Picasso, of varying quality. Of those listed below, Richardson's is by far the most reliable and up-to-date, though so far it has only reached 1932. The others listed here are readable and offer different perspectives or biases.

Pierre Daix, *Picasso: Life and Art*, trans. Olivia Emmett (London: Thames and Hudson, 1993)

Patrick O'Brian, *Picasso* (London: Collins, 1976)

Roland Penrose, *Picasso: His Life and Work* (Harmondsworth: Pelican, 1971)

John Richardson (with Marilyn McCully), *A Life of Picasso* [3 vols] (London: Pimlico 1991, 1996; London: Cape, 2007)

MEMOIRS

There are a number of memoirs of Picasso written by former

mistresses, relatives or friends. Here are a few of the most important – or the most gripping.

Françoise Gilot and Carlton Lake, *Life with Picasso* (London: Virago, 1990)

Fernande Olivier, *Picasso and His Friends* (London: Heinemann, 1964)

Hélène Parmelin, *Picasso Plain* (London: Secker and Warburg, 1964)

Marina Picasso, *My Grandfather* (London: Riverhead, 2002)

Jaime Sabartés, *Picasso: An Intimate Portrait* (London: Allen, 1946)

Olivier Widmaier Picasso, *Picasso: The Real Family Story* (London: Prestel, 2004)

WRITINGS

Ashton's fascinating anthology is organized thematically and contains the most important published interviews as well as recorded statements. Bernadac and Piot is the reference point for all of Picasso's poetry.

Dore Ashton (ed.), *Picasso on Art* (London: Thames and Hudson, 1973)

Marie-Laure Bernadac and Christine Piot (eds.), *Picasso: Collected Writings* (New York: Abbevile, 1989)

CRITICISM

There is one essential anthology that gives an insight into Picasso's critical fortunes.

Marilyn McCully (ed.), *A Picasso Anthology: Documents, Criticism, Reminiscences* (London: Arts Council of Great Britain, 1981)

OEUVRE CATALOGUES

Picasso's work was catalogued early on by Zervos, whose 33-volume project although incomplete and confusing remains fundamental. Other catalogues attempting to give a complete view of the artist's work include Chipp/Wofsy and the on-line project run by Enrique Mallen. But some of the most important catalogues focus on a single strand of the artist's

work: printmaking in the case of
Geiser/Baer and sculpture in the
case of Spies/Piot. The various
catalogues (not listed here) of
the collections in the Picasso
museums in Antibes, Barcelona,
Málaga and especially Paris are
also extremely useful.

**Herschel B. Chipp and Alan
Wofsy** (eds.) *The Picasso Project*
[13 vols] (San Francisco: Alan
Wofsy Fine Arts, 1995–2004)
**Bernhard Geiser/Brigitte
Baer**, *Picasso: Peintre-Graveur,
Catalogue raisonné de l'oeuvre gravé
et lithographié et des monotypes*,
vols i–ii (Bern: Kornfeld, 1990,
1992) and **Brigitte Baer**, *Picasso:
Peintre-Graveur, Catalogue raisonné
de l'oeuvre gravé*, vols iii–vii (Bern:
Kornfeld, 1992–6)
**Arnold Glimcher and Marc
Glimcher** (eds.), *Je Suis le
Cahier: The Sketchbooks of Picasso*
(London: Royal Academy of
Arts, 1986)
**Werner Spies and Christine
Piot**, *Picasso Sculpteur, Catalogue
raisonné* (Paris: Centre
Pompidou, 2000)

Christian Zervos, *Pablo Picasso*,
[33 vols] (Paris: Cahiers d'Art,
1932–1978)
On-line Picasso Project, http://
picasso.tamu.edu/picasso/

EXHIBITION CATALOGUES
Barr's 1939 catalogue set a new
standard for Picasso scholars.
Recent catalogues have been
among the most important venues
for writing on the artist's work.

Anne Baldessari et al, *Matisse-
Picasso* (London: Tate Gallery,
2002)
Alfred H. Barr, *Picasso: Forty
Years of His Art* (New York:
Museum of Modern Art, 1939)
Marie-Laure Bernadac et al,
Late Picasso (London: Tate
Gallery, 1988)
**Elizabeth Cowling and John
Golding**, *Picasso: Sculptor/Painter*
(London: Tate Gallery, 1994)
Marilyn McCully (ed.), *Picasso:
The Early Years 1892–1906*
(Washington D.C.: National
Gallery of Art, 1997)
Marilyn McCully (ed.), *Picasso:
Painter and Sculptor in Clay*

(London: Royal Academy of
Arts, 1998)

Steven Nash (ed.), *Picasso and
the War Years 1937–1945* (London:
Thames and Hudson, 1998)

William Rubin (ed.), *Picasso and
Portraiture* (London: Thames and
Hudson, 1996)

Jean Sutherland Boggs, *Picasso
and Things* (Cleveland Museum
of Art, 1992)

THEMATIC MONOGRAPHS

Here are a few of the many
important studies of aspects of
Picasso's work. Karmel, Green
and Florman deploy challenging
but rewarding theoretical
approaches.

Anne Baldessari, *Picasso and
Photography: The Dark Mirror*,
trans. Deke Dusinbere (Paris:
Flammarion, 1997)

Lisa Florman, *Myth and
Metamorphosis: Picasso's Classical
Prints of the 1930s* (London: MIT,
2000)

Susan Grace Galassi, *Picasso's
Variations on the Old Masters:
Confrontations with the Past* (New

York: Abrams, 1996)

Christopher Green, *Picasso:
Architecture and Vertigo* (London:
Yale, 2006)

Pepe Karmel, *Picasso and the
Invention of Cubism* (London:
Yale, 2003)

Peter Read, *Picasso and
Apollinaire: The Persistence of
Memory* (Berkeley: University of
California Press, 2008)

Gertje Utley, *Picasso: The
Communist Years* (London: Yale,
2000)

STUDIES OF SINGLE WORKS

Two of the most significant
paintings by Picasso have been
the subject of many books and
articles. The books below each
give a comprehensive view of
the work in question.

Herschel B. Chipp,
*Picasso's Guernica: History,
Transformations, Meanings*
(California Studies in the History
of Art, No 26, 1988)

William Rubin et al, *Picasso: Les
Demoiselles d'Avignon* (New York:
Museum of Modern Art, 1994)

INDEX